14 95

D1601996

Text and Original Paintings by Abel O'Keragori
Edited by Bridget A. C. King
Graphic Design by Susan Scull-Carvalho, Katherine
Mamai and Abby J. Levine

Published by JACARANDA DESIGNS, LTD.
Post Office Box 76691, Nairobi, Kenya
Copyright © by Jacaranda Designs, Ltd.
First Published 1995

ISBN 9966-884-74-2

Typeset in Palatino, Goudy and StonePrint Italic. Printed by Singapore National Printers.

Preface

The Abagusii are a Bantu, Ekugusii speaking people who live predominantly in Kisii and Nyamira Districts of the Nyanza Province of Kenya. Post-independence migrations of the Abagusii were caused mainly by population pressure and a consequent desire for more agricultural land. This move saw them settle in other parts of Kenya such as the Rift Valley and the Eastern and Coastal provinces where they engage in various commercial activities.

The grouping of the Abagusii among other Bantu tribes is rationalised by a number of factors but is mainly determined by their language and culture. These show a marked resemblance to other ethnic communities such as the Kuria, Embu, Meru, Kikuyu and Luhya of Kenya, the Baganda of Uganda and the Nyamwezi of Tanzania (Whiteley 1960). The pre-colonial socio-political and economic organization of these communities is also said to share a number of features common to those of the Abagusii.

According to tradition, the Abagusii originated in a place called 'Misiri', an area just to the north of Mount Elgon. Around 1560 they moved southwards and settled at Goge, in Yimbo location of the present day Siaya District of Nyanza Province. After some time, their migration continued to Kisumu, probably as a result of over-population and cattle raids. Serious famine in 1650 caused a further migration from Kisumu to Kano. Here the Abagusii settled, for the River Enyando and its tributaries gave flowing water, providing good grass for the livestock and plentiful game for hunting. Also around this time some of the Abagusii were taken into slavery by the Luo people, remaining there for several generations. Later they moved northwards to the cool western highlands of Kenya where they presently live.

During their dispersal and these early settlement periods, sons of Mogusii, the great-great-grandfather of the Abagusii, encountered some animals and natural phenomena with which

they later identified themselves. These became the various totems of the different clans. The Abagusii can be divided into four main groups: Abasweta, Abagirango, Ababasi and Abanchari who are descendants of Mosweta, Mochorwa, Mobasi and Monchari respectively. The Abagirango or Abachorwa took *engo*, the leopard, as their totem, thereby giving each group a criterion for exogamy and a sense of kinship, identity in battle and an obligation among its members to help and protect each other.

The Abagusii believed in a supreme God, Engoro, who guided and assisted them in their migration. He saved them from their enemies and natural calamities. According to tradition, Engoro was the original progenitor and source of prosperity and life who sent rain or drought, plenty or famine, health or disease, peace or war. They also believed in supernatural ancestral spirits, regarded as immortal beings who were always in touch with the living. These were agents of Engoro and intervened on his behalf. The Sun, the Moon and the Stars were also agents of Engoro through which Engoro observed and shepherded the activities of man. Prayers were directed to Engoro through the Sun. When a child was born, the Sun was requested to take care of it.

Folklore is the mainstay of the Abagusii history and cultural way of life. Historical material has always been handed down orally from one generation to another. In pre-colonial times, *emegano* (folk tales or stories)were told to the children by old people, particularly grandparents, after the evening meal and around the fireplace. Children were told not to tell stories during the day or else they would not grow taller but remain dwarfs. This was to discourage them from being idle or lazy. The Abagusii have articulate philosophies of life which are communicated through riddles, folk tales, songs, proverbs and poems. Before storytelling commences, the narrator says *Mogano ngocha nde*, 'Story I am coming'. When the listeners reply *Mogano nchuo*, 'Let the story come', the storytelling may begin. When the narration ends, the listeners, usually small children, get up after sitting for a long time and stretch their arms above their heads and say *Too inkine buna Emanga ne Esameta* or 'Let me grow like Manga and Semeta', the two highest hills in Kisii.

The Abagusii are agriculturalists. Growing cash crops like tea, coffee and pyrethrum is the main economic activity of the community. However, food crops such as maize, bananas, millet, potatoes, cassava and beans are also widely grown. Poultry and dairy farming distinguish the Abagusii who attach much importance to livestock, particularly cattle and goats. Such animals occupy a special place in the cultural life of the community and their ownership is indicative of the perceived level of social status, of men in particular. To an extent the possession of livestock is still an integral aspect of socio-cultural transactions. Livestock may, even now, become a part of the dowry upon marriage.

Okeng'o Matiang'i,
Department of Literature, University of Nairobi, 1994.

Riddles, *ebitandagwiri*...

are told in the evening, sometimes just before storytelling sessions, sometimes just after. They are told as a means of entertainment, of passing time, and also of testing quickness of wit and alertness of mind.

Kamura Gasinini, ka na itimo riamorwani...
> *Enchoke*

The little boy, with a warrior's spear...
> A bee

Onkune, nakuunekire...
> *Ekiebunda*

If you touch me I will put on the lid...
> Ekiebunda

Note: A small plant that folds up if touched or disturbed by either human or animal.

Eeri ya tata ekare bomanyi...
> *Engera*

My father's bull in Maasailand...
> A buffalo

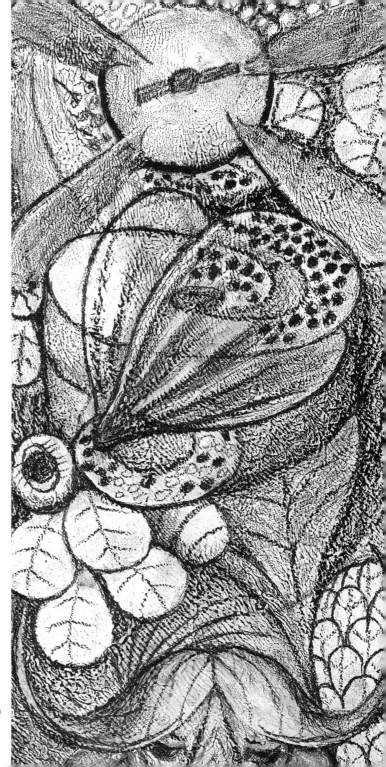

Mobasi Onchage
Son of Zebra

From lands far beyond the sunset came Mogusii, father of the Abagusii. For many moons he had chased the sunrise in search of good land with plentiful water and fertile soil. At last he came to a river flowing with crystal clear water and surrounded by green hills, flowers and fruit trees. Calling the river Omogusi after himself, the name it still bears, this river marks the boundary between Gusiiland and Luoland.

After many seasons of living on this fertile land, the Abagusii grew more numerous. Sons left their fathers' homesteads and settled hither and thither, wherever they could find good land to sustain their families.

One of these sons was Mobasi, a man renowned for the unusual habit of skinning his kills by starting at the back of the neck instead of at the underside as is normally the practice.

1

Mobasi found good lands south east of Inani, beyond the settlements of Mogirango and neighbouring the lands of the Kiligori Maasai.

Seeing new herds of cattle competing for grazing on their lands, the Kiligori Maasai, nomadic herdsmen who possessed countless cattle of their own, resented their new neighbours. The Maasai planned a raid on Mobasi's herds and one moonlit night, they stole all the cows belonging to Mobasi

Following the spoor of his missing herd next morning, Mobasi could tell that the raiding Maasai *morans* or warriors were too numerous for his family to confront alone. Beating out a message on the talking drums, he summoned his brothers to supply re-inforcements from the great clans of the Mogirango. The Abagusii warriors coloured their faces and clothing in ochre, the *chinkororo* regalia of the hunter, and when a sufficient number were gathered, set off in pursuit of their cattle.

Many days and nights went by before they caught up with the fleeing Maasai raiders. A furious fight ensued. Silent deaths were suffered as the arrows, spears and sling shots of the combatants constantly found their mark. Many were slain on both sides in violent hand to hand combat, the ground becoming slippery with the blood and guts of those who were slain. From that day until now, the battle ground has become known as *Mara* or the place of guts, *amara* being the Ekegusii word for 'guts'.

2

In the meantime, an armed group of Abagusii crept behind Maasai lines, helping themselves to as many cattle as they could manage and driving them away from the unprotected *manyattas*. This action they felt was fully justified when they considered the number of Abagusii warriors who had died as a result of the Maasai raid. Mobasi's son, also named Mobasi, was one of the raiding party.

Owing to a stomachache, brought on by eating rotten fruit during the long journey, the young Mobasi was left behind by his peers. Suffering constant agony over the next few days, the youth was not able to travel far. When at last he reached the *Mara* battleground, young Mobasi found a menacing group of *morans* approaching him. Immediately identifying Mobasi as an enemy by the Gusii pattern on his hippo hide shield, the Maasai *morans* gave chase. Still weak from his illness, Mobasi was not able to run fast. Fearing for his life, he prayed to Engoro, the god of the Gusii people, surrendering himself into his care.

Engoro must have heard the prayers of the young Mobasi, for just as the Maasai *morans* were preparing to add the boy's slight body to those being devoured by hyenas and vultures, a multitude of stampeding zebra and wildebeest burst across the open plains. Mobasi, as quick witted and as agile as a cheetah, took out a length of rope from beneath his robe. Looping it under his shoulders and around his shield, he threw a larger loop across the neck of a fleeing zebra. Hanging on tightly beneath its neck as it galloped away, Mobasi talked quietly and reassuringly to the striped beast.

It is said that if a wild animal cannot smell the blood of animals in a human being, it will treat that man as his friend. Mobasi had never eaten meat in his life. As he talked quietly to the zebra, it seemed to understand the boy's great need and stood still for a few minutes. This was enough time for Mobasi to loop two more lengths of rope over the back of the zebra and around the hippo hide shield. Safely cocooned between the zebra's belly and the strong skin of the shield, Mobasi was hidden from view.

As the zebra sped off to catch up with the stampeding herds, Mobasi's life was saved. The puzzled Maasai could find no trace of their foe, although no tree or bush was big enough to hide him. Shaking their heads in wonder, they went on their way.

Frightened by the smell of the bloody plains they had crossed, the terrified herds of zebra and wildebeest had disappeared from sight. The zebra and his human burden were alone as they made their way to the safety of the Lambwe valley. Here Mobasi bade the zebra stop for a while. Both man and beast drank thirstily from the river and rested in the shade of the great trees, for both were exhausted after their escape.

Mobasi talked so soothingly to the zebra that it became more confident in the young man. Soon, the two became firm companions and stayed together for many days.

Setting off finally in the direction of home, Mobasi feared a return to the *Mara*. Taking a circuitous route through Kurialand, Luoland and Mogirango, he finally reached his home. Mobasi entered his father's homestead riding his striped *enchage*, surprising everyone greatly. His family assumed that the young man had already become a pile of bleached bones on the bloody plains, for a month had passed since he had last been seen. Proudly, Mobasi introduced *enchage* his zebra friend to his bemused family. In grateful thanks for saving his life, Mobasi swore to protect the zebra and his descendants for evermore.

> "I, Mobasi, Son of Zebra
> I, who was saved by Zebra
> Fearing no man,
> Swear that whosoever kills a Zebra
> Will never find shelter in my home.
> Nor will they be served with food or drink
> But will be sent away
> Or killed like a traitor."

The Ababasi are still called Sons of Zebra for if the zebra had not saved this particular son of Mobasi, there would be no Ababasi people alive today.

Riddles, *ebitandagwiri*...

Omongina, omotengera ebate...

Etinga ya' roche

The old lady dancer, in the small valley...

A water mill

Note: Water mills used to be very common in days before electricity was introduced. Now few remain, but the grain ground by water mill is highly prized as superior.

O'Monchari O'Mache

People of the Hippopotamus

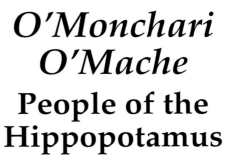

Monto, the father of all men, was the son of the god Engoro. Engoro ruled the heavens and his messengers were the Sun by day and the Moon and Stars by night. Monto had a wife, N'gina Monto, and many sons and daughters. After some time they became too many for the land and the young men and women were forced to leave their home in Misiri and search for lands elsewhere. Three of the sons of Monto travelled together; they were Mogusii, Moluya and Mogikoyo.

After travelling for many years, the three brothers finally reached the eastern shores of Lake Victoria. In the highlands to the east of the great lake, Mogusii, son of Monto, found a land rich with forests, green pastures and crystal clear waters. He called the place Inani. Legend has it that the remains of Mogusii are buried within the borders of the great forest of Inani. Mogusii had many sons: Onchari, Ogetutu, Nyaribari, Mobasi, Omachoge and Mogira 'Ngo. The sons of Mogusii became known as the Abagusii.

"Mogano ngocha nde"   **Story I'm coming**
'Mogano inchuo'.   **Story come.**

In those distant days there were many wars. During one particularly violent skirmish, Onchari, son of Mogusii, was killed. Monchari, his young wife, was expecting their second child. On the very day Onchari died, the shock of his death caused the young woman to give birth to her baby. She called her new born son Onchari, believing him to be the reincarnation of her dead husband.

Without the protection of a husband and not wishing to marry again, Monchari courageously left her homestead to seek support from her relatives in Maragoli (known by the Abagusii as Boragori). Taking her daughter and infant son, Monchari arrived safely in Boragori where she was welcomed by members of her family and stayed for two years. When the time finally came to travel to Inani to rejoin her husband's family, she and her two children bravely set off again.

Monchari embarked on the hazardous journey knowing that leopard, lion, hyena and other dangerous wild beasts roamed freely in the country she had to cross. Hostile warriors, fierce and well armed, would attack on sight if they found her travelling alone. To stay clear of these perils, Monchari and her children followed the banks of *Nyanch*a, the big river. For many moons, the river became her guide and source of life

As she travelled, heavy rains to the east caused the river to rise suddenly, turning it into a raging torrent. Monchari searched desperately for the safety of higher land, but there was none. Rushing waters began to flood the land, sweeping away everything in their path and waves of flood water swept away the three weary travellers. Holding on tightly to her two children, Monchari prayed to Engoro, the god of her grandparents, to save her. As the flood waters closed over her head, she touched something beneath her feet. As firm as an island, the form arose, bearing Monchari's wife and her two children safely out of the water.

14

"Engoro has answered my prayer," she gasped, "by sending a hippo to save us. But how can such a fearsome and dangerous beast save our lives?" wondered Monchari in awe.

The mighty beast with small flapping ears, bright eyes and immense jaws, carried the frightened family to dry land. Sensing their terror, the huge creature calmed Monchari with these words: "It is true that I am strong and ugly, huge and fearsome, but I am not truly dangerous," said the hippo. "Only when danger threatens me do I rise up in anger and snap my mighty jaws. Nothing that moves in peace will be harmed by me. Thus will it always be."

"I know that Engoro has sent you in answer to my prayer," replied Monchari. "But I have been in fear for so long, it is difficult to put my trust in a wild animal."

"Do not be afraid. No harm shall come to you this day, for I will protect you and be a father to your children," the hippo gently reassured her.

Monchari and her children were relieved at the kind words of the hippo. For many moons they stayed with the mighty animal as it moved slowly towards Inani. During the day they travelled on it's back through the cool waters, keeping out of the heat of the sun. At night they rested on a dry bank while the hippo grazed calmly around them. They ate fruits and wild herbs from the forest, drank from the fast flowing waters of the river and were shielded from harm and inclement weather by the immense body of their foster father, the hippo.

For some time they followed the course of the river through forests, ravines and more floods until they arrived finally in Inani. Entering the homestead astride their protector, the hippo, the family was received with shock. Frightened, the women and children fled from this strange apparition.

"Abanto baito kanyeka" Monchari called to them. "My people, be calm."

When they were sure that the beast was not hostile, the elders called the community to return. The elders were curious to find out why Monchari was in the company of a hippo, so they invited her to stand before them. In response to their questions, Monchari praised the hippo as the father of her family, answering:

Monchari Omache,
Chindiba chibokendu
Chikogenda boira bokia
Otairogeti Gesiomba

We are the Abanchari people
Sons of the deep waters
That flow by day and night
Without fear of revenge.

Oyo ogoita Engubo
Tacha Minto anywe Mache
Negesaku Akuname

He who kills a hippo will not enter into our house
Nor will we give him even a drink of water
As he kneels in the cold of our doorway.

These words shocked the elders, for to deprive a traveller of water is to deprive him of life. Monchari explained how the hippo had saved her family from the floods. For this reason she had sworn never again to kill a hippo nor to eat its meat, for the mighty hippo was now the father of her children.

The elders of Inani respected Monchari as the mother of the grandson of Mogusii, their own ancestor. They awarded her with a gift of land between the Omogusi and the Riyabe rivers, good land where many clear streams and springs flow. No matter how severe the drought elsewhere might be, this source of water would never dry up. Monchari led the hippo, the protector of her family, to the safe waters of the Omogusi River. From that day on, hippos have roamed the land between the Omogusi and the Riyabe rivers, the land of their people.

Young Onchari grew to be a skilful hunter of lion, elephant, rhino and buffalo, but he remembered always to protect the hippo from other hunters. Whenever he found a dead hippo he cried as if it were his own kin. Asking to be given the skin, he dried and treated it, shaping the hide into a protective shield. This he kept as a reminder of the way that the mighty hippo had shielded his family from harm in those far off days. To this day strong hippo shields are still made by Onchari Omache of the Abagusii. From generation to generation, the Abanchari have vowed never to hunt or to kill the hippo.

This story has been handed down to our children so that they might know the importance of the hippo as father and saviour of the Abanchari people.

'Nto 'nkine 'nkine buna Emanga ne Esameta'.
'Let me grow as tall as the hills of Emanga and Esameta.'

Mogira Ngo
Protector of the Leopard

Long ago lived Mogusii, said to be the father of six sons; Ogetutu, Nyaribari, Mobasi, Omachoge, Mogira and Onchari. By and by, Mogusii's sons married and moved away from the homestead at Inani to make their own homes. They took with them their wives and children and settled on new lands.

Ogetutu moved due north of Inani, while Nyaribari occupied lands to the north east. Mobasi and Omachoge moved south east and Mogira moved due north beyond Ogetutu. Onchari did not move, but took lands around Inani. Carrying with them new grain for planting and livestock, the brothers worked hard. The six sons regularly visited their parents, taking with them gifts which they offered with dutiful pleasure to the old folk.

Mogira, however, became a hunter… and this is where our tale begins.

Mogira the hunter did not eat the meat of the cow, the goat or the chicken. He much preferred the game meat of the wild animals which roamed the vast plains and forests. When the game moved up from the *Mara* to the Gusii highlands in search of better pasture and water, Mogira would follow them, hunting all manner of beasts; elephant, lion, leopard, hippo, buffalo and even the smaller antelope. He helped the Omogusii drive off those animals which destroyed their crops and he bravely fought the lion, leopard, rhino and buffalo when they threatened human life.

When Mogira died he left two sons, each named Mogira after their father. They were known as Mogira Motambe[1], the taller, and Mogira Mweng'e[2], the shorter. Mogira Motambe's mother died when he was just a few days old, so his father decided to marry again to provide a mother for his infant son. To begin with, the second wife was very kind to Mogira Motambe, but when her own son was born she turned against the older boy. Mogira Motambe was more handsome, healthier, stronger and better looking than his step brother Mogira Mweng'e. The second wife grew more and more jealous that her own son was less favoured and began to look for ways to improve his position.

As the two boys grew up they became inseparable. Mogira Mweng'e looked up to his older brother with admiration, and Mogira Motambe proudly took good care of the younger boy. Taught by their father, the two boys soon became expert hunters. They improved the old man's weapons and hunting techniques and even introduced to the community the practice of hollowing out tree trunks to collect honey.

As old Mogira's life drew to an end, he felt immense pride in his two sons and wished them both well in life. On his death, the two sons behaved with great respect, performing all the rites of burial as custom and tradition demanded. However, when the funeral rites were over, the second wife gave the *ekerogo*, the inheritance stool, to her own son instead of respecting ancient tradition and giving it to Mogira Motambe, the first born.

Not long after their father's burial, the two brothers went out hunting together as usual. When Mogira Motambe climbed a tree to collect honey for the midday meal he heard a leopard roar fiercely at the base of the tree. He called out to Mogira Mweng'e to kill the leopard and save him from attack, but instead of coming to his aid, Mogira Mweng'e ignored his brother's plea. Collecting up his weapons he walked away without a word, leaving his older brother in mortal danger. Shocked, Mogira Motambe realised for the first time that Mogira Mweng'e had fallen under his step-mother's evil influence and it would not be safe for him to return home.

Forced to defend himself against the angry leopard, Mogira Motambe summoned the wisdom of Engoro, the god of his grandfathers and of all earthly creatures. Talking to the leopard in a gentle voice he said: "I am unarmed and alone. Surely you would not attack a defenceless opponent? Such a thing would be beneath your dignity."

The snarling leopard ignored this plea and was only deterred from climbing the tree by the many honey bees whose stings he feared. Mogira Motambe decided on another approach. "If you let me to go in peace, I vow never again to hunt you or your family for either skins or meat. If, however, you attack me, I shall beat upon this hive and the bees will kill us both."

After hours of besieging Mogira Motambe in the tree, the leopard seemed to make a decision. With one final snarl, it backed away and disappeared into the bush. Mogira Motambe came down the tree with plenty of honey and began to live peacefully in the forest on his own. Several times he came across the leopard while hunting and each time he gave the creature a little of the meat which he had caught. From that time Mogira Motambe kept his sacred vow to respect the leopard. He even changed his name to Mogira Ngo, the one who refuses to kill or eat the leopard.

As time passed and neither harmed the other, the hunter and the leopard family became friends. When the leopardess gave birth to three cubs and dared not go far to hunt for fear of the scavenging hyena, Mogira Ngo often killed an extra antelope to feed the hungry mother. If he saw a hyena approaching the place where the cubs were kept, Mogira Ngo would drive it angrily away.

When he remembered how his half-brother had left him to die he felt very bitter, but after many seasons of living alone in the forest, Mogira Ngo decided that he was old enough and strong enough to confront his step-mother and half-brother. Never once had he allowed himself to be seen by villagers in the forest, deliberately keeping

away from all human contact. He returned home to his village, thinking his people must believe him long dead. Privately, he vowed not to kill Mogira Mweng'e but to drive him and his wicked mother out of their home.

Carrying several spears, a hippo hide shield, a bow and some arrows, Mogira Ngo entered the village dressed in elephant skin and antelope hide. He had become a tall, muscular and hairy man of great stature who commanded instant respect. After so many years away, no one in the village recognised him. Ignorant of his real identity, Mogira Mweng'e's wife accorded Mogira Ngo the traditional welcome due to such an impressive stranger and his nephews and nieces gazed at him in awe.

When asked his name he replied that it was Ngo. His brother's wife told him that her husband was Mogira Mweng'e, son of Mogira, son of Mogusii and brother of the late Mogira Motambe. She added that her mother-in-law had died some months ago. Mogira Ngo did not reveal his true identity, but listened to this news with an outward lack of emotion.

Two nights later Mogira Mweng'e came home. Hearing of the stranger's arrival he went with trepidation to the guest hut. Although not certain that his brother had died, he and his mother had conspired to deceive their relatives, relating how a fierce leopard had attacked and eaten the older boy. In sorrow, the relatives had believed the story. Now Mogira Mweng'e learned that a man by the name of Ngo, the leopard, had entered his compound and he was afraid. Creeping into the hut, he lit a rush torch. In the light of the flame he looked down in dismay at the face of his elder brother. Running back to his hut in a panic Mogira Mweng'e packed up all his goods. He woke up his wife and children and without explanation led them from the village under the cloak of darkness, striking off towards the south in the hope that no-one would detect his shame.

In the morning, Mogira Ngo woke up to an empty home. Realising what must have happened while he had slept, he regretted that Mogira Mweng'e had left in such a cowardly manner. Being the fine hunter he was, he could detect the scent of his long-lost brother. For many months Mogira Ngo tracked his brother remorselessly. When he finally found him hiding in Gusii's extreme southern territory, the older brother addressed the younger man firmly:

"I will forgive your treachery," he promised his quaking brother, "but your evil deed will not be forgotten. I will continue to live in the north, taking a half of the livestock you have left behind. You will remain here in the south. To seal our agreement I demand that never again will you kill or injure a leopard; never again will you eat its flesh nor trade its skin for fur. This you must promise if our bond is to last. To seal the agreement you will give me five bulls and several heifers and all the lands in the north."

Mogira Mweng'e reluctantly agreed to abide by his brother's ruling. Since that time the two original Abagira Ngo leopard clans of the Abagusii people have remained separate, one in the north and the other in the south of Gusii.

Footnotes
[1] *Motambe: otherwise known as Nyamakabe*
[2] *Mweng'e: otherwise known as Motabori*

31

Igena Ku – Igena Mu
Come Forth, Baboons

Long ago, in the land of Gusii, there were only goats, cows, sheep, chickens and some song birds, but no baboons.

This is the story of how baboons came to exist in the land of Gusii.

In a certain village near the forest of Inani, the Riyabe River rushes down rocky rapids, coming to rest as tranquil waters in a most beautiful and scenic land. This was once the favourite place of ten sisters.

The young maidens' work was to help their mother fetch water, gather firewood and cook good food. Every afternoon, after finishing their daily chores, the sisters would go to the river to bathe. After washing, they loved to sit on the warm boulders worn smooth by generations of young women with softly oiled skins.

Nine of these maidens were beautiful but the last born was not; pock marks scarred her face and made her the subject of mocking abuse from her unkind sisters. However, the unfortunate girl accepted her deformity stoically, believing it to be part of Engoro's plan.

One afternoon, the ten girls spent longer than normal bathing and basking on the rocky banks of the river. There was one particular stone that the girls liked above all others for the top of this stone was curved over in such a way that it provided shade from the full heat of the sun. As the sisters lay there in the shade, chatting to each other and resting after their morning's toil, there appeared a strange old crone. She was so ugly that even the birds were frightened away. Unmoved, the girls continued to polish their nails and smooth their bodies with aromatic oils made from herbs and wild fruits.

Slowly the old woman hobbled to the foot of the curved stone, leaning heavily on her stick. "Spare me some of your oil," she pleaded. The sisters listened to her pitiful request with contempt. Only the youngest found sympathy in her heart for the old woman whose ancient skin was covered with open scabs and weeping sores. The foul smell emanating from the wounds had attracted clouds of buzzing and irritating flies. The last born felt great pity for the poor woman but was afraid of appearing too sympathetic in case her cruel and selfish sisters would further shun her company.

Quietly the youngest sister sorrowed for the old woman. Regardless of the consequences, she took out her goatskin bag of oil and stepped down to speak to the old crone. "I will anoint you, old woman," she said kindly, "but first, come with me to wash in the river."

Leading her by the hand, the last born took the old woman to the river where she washed both her ancient body and her clothes. Sitting the Old One down on a flat stone, the youngest sister gently oiled the worn and wrinkled body until the flesh began to soften. As the oil was rubbed into the old woman's skin, the weeping scabs and sores seemed miraculously to disappear until her skin began to glow like that of a young woman. Watching in amazement, the older girls saw that the skin of their youngest sister was also losing its blemishes and becoming fresh and clear. The older girls became envious of the now beautiful young woman and turned their abuse to her.

When the last born had finished all her oil, the Old One stood up and smiled at her. "Thank you, my daughter, for your great kindness. Engoro has rewarded you a thousandfold. Go! Look at your reflection in the river."

Moving across to the foot of the curved stone where the nine sisters lay, the Old One turned on them in anger. Stretching out her arm with fingers opened wide, she cursed them. "For your vanity and heartless lack of sympathy, you will from now on be called *chingoge*, baboons. Your skin will be coarse and hairy and your voices harsh and shrill; the forest will be your only home and wild fruits your only food."

The girls laughed and mocked, "You can't harm us. You're a nobody. Be gone!" they jeered.

"*Igena Ku*," chanted the old woman in a commanding voice. "Big rock, cover them.". With a loud crack the curved stone fell, completely covering the nine sisters from view. "*Igena Mu*," she chanted again, striking the rock with her gnarled stick. "Big Rock, free them."

The stone fell away at the sound of her voice and nine long-tailed, yellow baboons leaped out. Leaping and squealing around the old woman in a frenzy, they begged her to change them back to their former selves. But the old woman simply disappeared. In this way did baboons come into being, a constant reminder of human unkindness, one to another.

The last born married Mosweta son of Mogusii. Her sons, Nyaribari, Ogetutu and Machoge became the Abasweta clan of the Abagusii people, taking the *engoge*, the baboon, as their totem in memory of their mother's lost sisters.

Ogetutu, Enda Y'enchogu

As Great as the Elephant's Tummy

Long, long ago, in the land of Inani in Gusii, lived Mogusii with his many sons. As their numbers grew greater and greater the sons and their wives and children had to move away from their father's home to look for wider pastures. Ogetutu was the first of the sons to move out of Inani, settling on lands directly north of his birthplace.

As the years passed, Ogetutu prospered in his new land Bogetutu. He sired many sons and daughters who married into other Gusii clans and in turn presented him with grand children and great grand children. By and by, Abagetutu had close relatives in all the Gusii clans of Abanyaribari, Ababasi, Abamachoge, Abagira'Ngo and Abanchari. There was no family in Gusii into which the Omogetutu had not married. Everyone in Gusii felt at ease with the Ogetutu and warmly welcomed the opportunity to marry into their family.

Ogetutu was well respected and dealt generously with the members of his family. He owned vast lands which were very fertile and flowed with a thousand springs of crystal clear water. Wild game roamed his territory in all seasons providing them with plentiful meat.

Ogetutu's descendants were, and still are, among the healthiest and tallest men in the land of Gusii. Tall, muscular, barrel chested, handsome and charismatic characters, they can talk until the Manga Hills tremble with their echoes. These men can sing and dance, wrestle and fight and act with justice when the need be so.

The women are blessed with almond eyes, wasp waists and chocolate skins that are truly African. Tall by normal standards, they walk straight with a natural elegance and gait that turns the heads of their many admirers.

In those far off days the people were beset by many epidemics. Typhoid, blackwater and yellow fever and numerous other diseases sent whole families fleeing from the affected areas to seek refuge elsewhere. On one occasion an epidemic wiped out more than half of the population of Gusii, affecting rich and poor, old and young alike. There was much sorrow at the many burials although few were left to bury the dead, many of the survivors being too weak to perform the sad task. When the epidemic abated, the people were weakened, food was scarce and everyone had lost some members of their family. Whole families had died out with only children or lone adults surviving. Grouping together for mutual protection, neighbours became relatives.

The elders that survived in each clan came together. They sent scouts to all parts of

Gusii to assess the damage and to carry out a census of survivors. The orphaned children needed homes and the old people needed taking care of; wives were needed for widowers and sires for the widows. At last the work was done and the elders were informed. Of all six clans, the Ogetutu had recovered the fastest and were best able to deal with the care that was needed. Without delay, the elders of the Ogetutu made an openhanded offer to all friends and relatives from the other clans to move to Bogetutu. So it was that people from all corners of Gusii migrated to the lands of Bogetutu.

As the years passed, the people recovered and many went back to their clans. However, many families in Bogetutu had adopted children from other clans whose members had perished . As these children became adults, they were given land and homes. The young women were married to other clans, just as if they were original Abagetutu. They grew up not knowing any other home and have become some of the most prominent families in Bogetutu. In the same manner, those Abagetutu who had surviving relatives in the other clans emigrated into those clans and became leading citizens of their new communities.

In the whole land of Gusii, the only clan that has members from all the other clans is the Bogetutu, thus earning themselves the great title of *Ogetutu Enda Y'Enchogu*. This title refers to their well known generosity, both in the past and still today. While others may have the generosity of a rat's stomach, those of the Ogetutu have proven themselves to have a heart 'as great as the stomach of the elephant'.

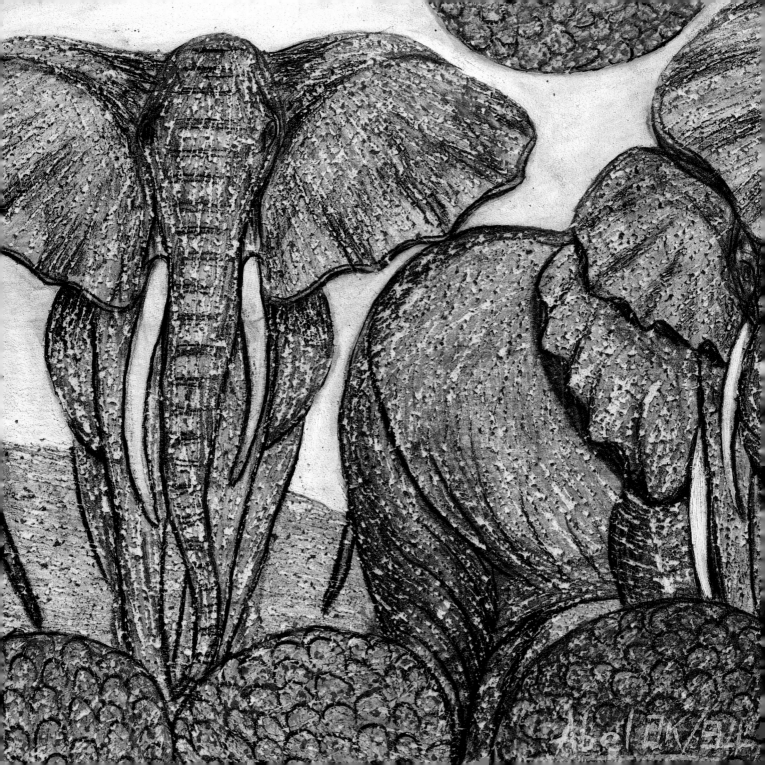

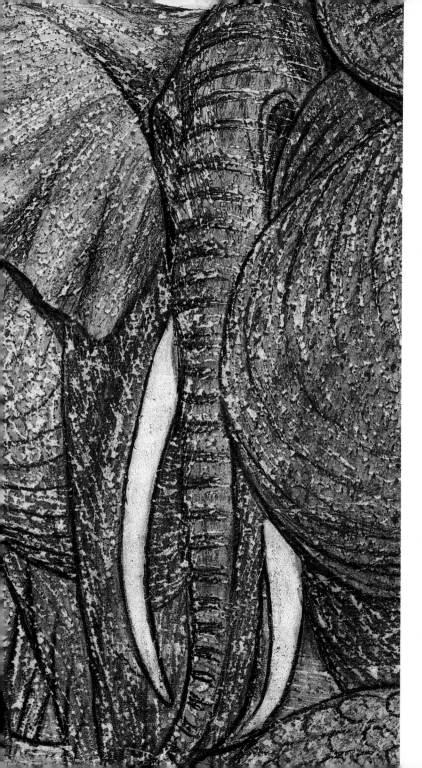

About the Artist

Abel O'Keragori was born in Gusii (Kisii) in 1952. He was referred to as an 'artist' from his very earliest days.

While attending the prestigious Cardinal Otunga High School, Abel started an Art Club with the support of the headmaster, the late Brother Innocent De Kok, who recognised the potential of his artwork.

After leaving High School, Abel took a degree in commerce and for many years worked as an accountant, not returning to the art scene until 1990 when his first child began to use crayons in her school work. This re-awakened Abel's passion for art and he slowly worked his way back into the field as a freelance artist. In 1994 he gave up his profession and became a full-time artist.

Abel has held two one-man shows in Kenya and has participated in innumerable group shows at home, in other African countries and overseas. His work is now held in private collections all over the world.

Abel is married and has three children. He has three brothers and three sisters.

His mother, the source of these stories, still lives in Kisii. His father died in 1992 at the age of 75.

Glossary

ABAGUSII (the people)	A Bantu settled agricultural community living in South Western Kenya. They are the descendants of Mugusii, a son of Monto. **Gusii** (the country) **Mogusii** (the person).
CHINKORORO	Literally, *'those who dressed in ochre'*. The face decorations and the clothing of the bravest hunters and warriors were coloured with natural ochre. Therefore, anyone wearing ochre was classified as a hunter or *chinkororo*.
CLAN	The term clan denotes a social grouping, bigger than a family, comprising a number of households, the male heads of which claim descent from a common ancestor. Gusii clans are exogamous, meaning marriage from within the clan is forbidden and regarded as incest.
EKEROGO	The traditional three-legged inheritance stool, passed on by a father, normally to his oldest son, as a physical sign that the recipient should inherit according to tradition.
EMANGA and **ESAMETA**	The tallest hills in the land of the Abagusii, thought to be the home of the spirits who bring succour to the people. During warfare they acted as a strategic point from which to survey the movements of the enemy.
ENGORO	The God of the Gusii people, the source of prosperity and life. The Abagusii are monotheist. During a time of famine or other calamity, sacrifices were offered to Engoro at sacred sites.
INANI	The great forest from which the community was nurtured. From this central point, the Abagusii gradually began their dispersal.
MANYATTA	A Kimaasai word relating to the special home of the Maasai morans.
MONTO	Father of all men, according to Abagusii mythology.
MORAN	A Kimaasai word for unmarried but circumcised young men or warriors who were trained and used as a standing army to protect the Maasai people from their enemies.
TOTEM	Functionally totems have a unifying role, especially as members of a totem clan would regard each other as kinsmen and were bound to help and protect each other. A totem is thus ancestral to the clan and to the individual. Because of its connection with the instituted morality, the totem is almost always hedged about with tabus of avoidance or strictly ritualised contact.
TRIBE	A tribe is a social group comprising a series of families, clans and adopted strangers. Members of a tribe include a common social group name, a relatively common culture or way of life, a common language or dialect and a general tradition of common descent. A sub-tribe denotes a division of a tribe which observes a common totem and claims common descent.